100% UNOFFICIAL GUIDE TO FORTNITE:

A CENTUM BOOK 978-1-913865-73-3
Published in Great Britain by Centum Books Ltd
This edition published 2021
1 3 5 7 9 10 8 6 4 2

We have produced this "100% Unofficial Guide To Fortnite" book
independently from Epic Games, Inc, the owner of FORTNITE®.
To be completely clear, this book has not been authorised, approved,
licensed, sanctioned or sponsored by Epic Games, Inc. Epic Games, Inc
owns all rights to FORTNITE products and trademarks.

Text and design © Centum Books | Images © Shutterstock & © Istock
Additional text and images are reproduced with permission from Cherry Lake
Publishing Group, 2395 South Huron Parkway, Suite 200, Ann Arbor, MI48104, USA
cherrylakepublishing.com

Produced by The Wonderful Ideas Project LTD with
Chris Caulfield (Words) and Nathan Balsom (Art).
Special consultants: Beau Chance, Elijah Caulfield,
Will Shepherd, Dylan & Brody Cardell

Centum Books Ltd, 20 Devon Square,
Newton Abbot, Devon, TQ12 2HR, UK
9/10 Fenian St, Dublin 2, D02 RX24, Ireland
books@centumbooksltd.co.uk

CENTUM BOOKS Limited Reg. No 07641486

A CIP catalogue record for this book is
available from the British Library.

Printed in China

100% UNOFFICIAL GUIDE TO
FORTNITE

THIS BOOK BELONGS TO

CONTENTS

CHARACTER CREATION

READY PLAYER ONE

To play Fortnite you need a character. Use this space to design your very own now. Remember to equip them with a harvesting tool, back bling and a weapon to look like a total pro!

NAME:

DATE:

PLAY!

FORTNITE: YOUR CHAPTER

Begin your journey by filling in some details about your ideal Fortnite look and style. Then when you've completed this book, come back and see if you've changed your mind.

FAVOURITE SKIN

FAVOURITE BACK BLING

FAVOURITE GLIDER

FAVOURITE WEAPON

FAVOURITE EMOTE

FAVOURITE HARVESTING TOOL

LOG IN: CREATE YOUR OWN ACCOUNT

KEEP IT REAL, KEEP IT FUN

Play at your own pace. It's easy to understand how gamers can get caught up in the exciting rush to unlock the newest skins and emotes. There is also a great sense of achievement in showing your friends that you've reached max level by donning extremely rare gear. Just don't let the chase take over your life. Remember, new cool stuff is always being added to Fortnite.

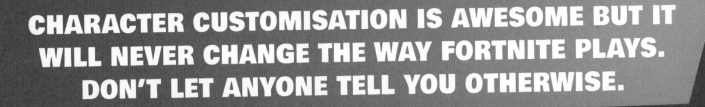

CHARACTER CUSTOMISATION IS AWESOME BUT IT WILL NEVER CHANGE THE WAY FORTNITE PLAYS. DON'T LET ANYONE TELL YOU OTHERWISE.

Just because you might have seen the best players sporting the rarest skins, emotes and back bling does not mean they have any impact on the gameplay. It's their skill and experience you are watching, nothing else. Wrapped weapons may look cool and interesting, but they do no more damage and are just as dangerous as regular weapons.

We play games to enjoy ourselves and have fun. The way Fortnite has brought people together is special and we don't want anything to get in the way of that. Rare outfits or dances are great but there is no need for jealousy or spending more than you can afford. The customisation in Fortnite is a bonus. The real joy comes from honing your skills, winning matches and playing with friends.

You can still complete challenges, win matches and level up your character through each season's tiers, without spending any money. So don't stress about how your character looks and have a blast.

WEEK 1 CHALLENGES

1 / 7

Complete any 4 challenges to earn the reward item

XP 5K

	Pick up an item of each rarity		✓
	Dance in different forbidden locations	0 / 7	★ 5
	Play matches with at least one elimination (HARD)	2 / 5	★ 10
1/3	Stage 1: Dance on top of a crown of RV's	0 / 1	★ 1
	Deal Headshot Damage to opponents	0 / 500	★ 5
1/3	Stage 1: Search Ammo Boxes in a single match (HARD)	0 / 5	★ 3
	Eliminate opponents in different Named Locations (HARD)	0 / 5	★ 10

BE UNIQUE

TO A NOOB, FORTNITE CAN BE AN OVERWHELMING WORLD FULL OF LIMITLESS CUSTOMISATION OPTIONS. FORTUNATELY, ALL THIS CAN BE BROKEN DOWN INTO A HANDFUL OF CATEGORIES, AND ARE ALL APPEARANCE-BASED.

EMOTES

Fortnite's fun emote animations are some of the most famous customisation options in the world. They range from elaborate dance moves, to gestures as simple as pumping your fist in the air. Emotes are also a great way to communicate with your teammates in Duo or Squad modes, especially if you aren't using a mic, as they can express just about any feeling. It doesn't have to all be serious though. Some are just there for a laugh.

BACK BLING

It was only a matter of time before Fortnite introduced back bling to its universe. In fact, the surprise was that it took until the Season 3 Battle Pass before we were introduced to their delights. Backpacks can be anything from skateboards to shields, or even sushi and disco balls! And, remember, like all customisations, they are only decorative.

WEAPON AND VEHICLE WRAPS

Why do the pros run around with different looking gear to those starting their Fortnite adventure? Simple. They've unlocked wraps to deck out their favourite weapons and vehicles. Launched in Season 7, wraps change the appearance of weapons and vehicles to match themes in the game. They do not provide any advantages.

GLIDER AND UMBRELLA SKINS

Back in the distant days of 2017, when Fortnite first launched itself on an unsuspecting world, gliders were one of the only cosmetics you could change. Today, there are countless ways to customise your loadouts but, back at the start, gliders were your go-to get-up to set yourself apart from the crowd. Covering everything from giant hamburgers to the infamous Flappy Flyer chicken, these are how every player floats down to the island.

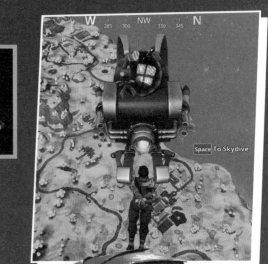

DID YOU KNOW?: THE SNOWFLAKE UMBRELLA IS PERHAPS THE RAREST GLIDER IN FORTNITE

HARVESTING TOOL SKINS

Customisable items help turn your trash monster into a fully themed loadout. Harvesting tool skins are no different. There is no doubt the pickaxe is one of the most important game mechanics inside Fortnite, but no matter what it looks like, the way you use it to harvest for building materials will not change. Turn to page 17 to see just how important they really are.

CONTRAIL SKINS

Did you know that you can even customise the visual effects surrounding your character as they skydive into battle?! That's right, you can kit-out your contrails. Contrails are those little lines that show you travelling through the air when not using a glider. While Flames might be the rarest skin, one of the most popular was Season 5 TP, where you got to leave a trail of toilet paper in your wake.

ROYALE RUMBLE

THE VIVID COLOURS ON THE SCREEN SCREAM ONE THING - IT'S THE FAST-PACED, FREEFORM, WORLD-BUILDING MULTIPLAYER MAYHEM SHOOTER UNLIKE ANYTHING YOU'VE PLAYED BEFORE.

IT'S BATTLE ROYALE!

READY UP

THE GOAL IS SIMPLE.
BE THE LAST ONE STANDING.

Your mission, and you'll want to accept it, is to load up on weapons, grab some great gear, and make sure you come out on top. So get on the battle bus, start the party, and skydive to your landing spot.

You may feel like a noob surrounded by overpowered superheroes but, armed with your 100% Unofficial Fortnite Annual, you might just score that precious

Victory Royale!

HUNT FOR GEAR

COMPLETE THIS GRID USING THE SIX PIECES OF GEAR BELOW. EACH ROW AND COLUMN SHOULD CONTAIN ONE OF EACH ITEM.

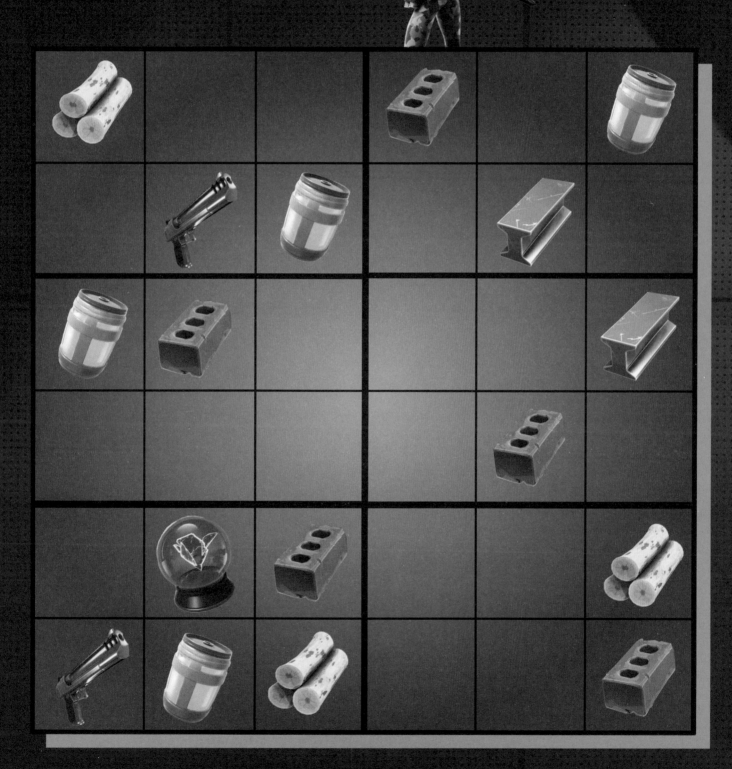

Answers on page 75

STAY INSIDE THE *STORM*

DANGER!

The timer has ticked down and you need to get to the final circle without taking any further damage. Only one Fortnite soldier can make it to the middle without running back into the deadly storm. Can you follow the paths taken by Raven, Astro Jack, Blaze, Peely and Midas to work out who grabs the Victory Royale?

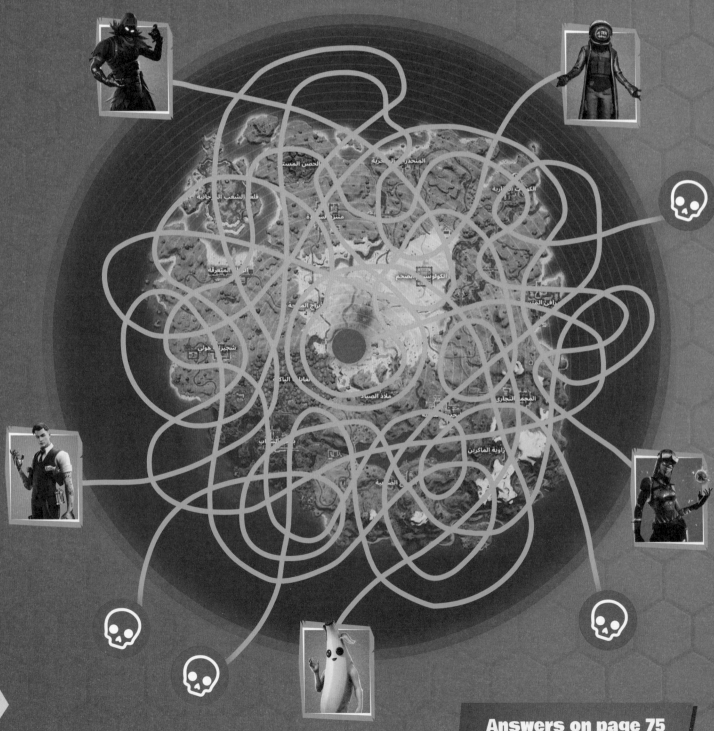

16

THE PICKAXE

EVERY PLAYER IN FORTNITE STARTS WITH THE SAME ITEM. THE HUMBLE PICKAXE MAY LOOK HARD TO USE BUT WITH PRACTICE THIS TRUSTY TOOL WILL SOON BE YOUR BEST FRIEND.

As well as being the most basic close-combat weapon in the game (warning: you will want to upgrade this IMMEDIATELY), the pickaxe allows you to smash and grab any object you find. Use it to help gather all those precious materials needed to build your way to the top.

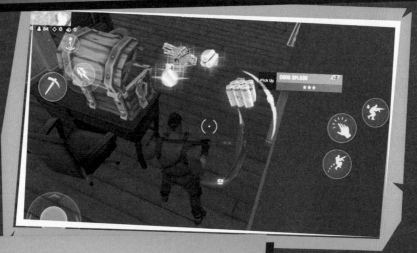

Some harvesting tools can be earned as you play. They look like their real-life counterparts, so expect to find plenty of hammers, axes and crowbars. Fortnite being Fortnite though, expect to also find plenty of weird and wonderful shapes from lollipops to wands, and everything in between.

WE'VE HIDDEN PICKAXES THROUGHOUT YOUR FORTNITE ANNUAL. CAN YOU FIND THEM ALL? HINT, YOU MAY HAVE ALREADY PASSED A FEW.

ODD ONE OUT

A SNIPER'S EYE IS NEEDED TO PICK OUT THE ONE IMPOSTER LURKING INSIDE EACH SUPER SQUAD BELOW. ONE CHARACTER IN EVERY PICTURE HAS HAD A SMALL CHANGE THAT MAKES THEM DIFFERENT TO THE ORIGINAL LINE UP. CAN YOU FIND ALL FOUR ODD ONES OUT?

ORIGINAL LINE UP

1

2

3

4

STARTING OUT

WHEN YOU FIRST ARRIVE ON THE ISLAND, YOU'LL BE ARMED WITH JUST YOUR TRUSTY PICKAXE. IF YOU WANT TO SURVIVE FOR MORE THAN FIVE MINUTES, YOU NEED TO UPGRADE YOUR WEAPONS, FAST.

Going up against heavily armed opponents will end badly, more often than not.

GRAB THE FIRST GUN YOU SEE, NO MATTER WHAT IT IS. IF YOU CAN'T SHOOT BACK, YOU ARE A SITTING DUCK.

If you are unlucky enough to land where no loot is lying around, find and head inside your nearest building. Remember you only have your harvesting tool at this stage, so will need to be extra careful as you scavenge the rooms for something, anything. **You can't afford to be picky.**

FORTUNATELY THE WORLD OF FORTNITE IS LITTERED WITH WEAPONRY, IT'S PART OF WHAT MAKES IT SUCH A GREAT GAME. SO IT WON'T BE LONG UNTIL YOU'RE ROCKING SOMETHING MUCH MORE POWERFUL!

ONE SUPER TIP:

Not all weapons are created equal. Grey guns are the most common in Fortnite. They will get you started, but you want to keep your eyes peeled for better kit. Look for green, blue and purple guns.

| COMMON |
| UNCOMMON |
| RARE |
| EPIC |
| LEGENDARY |
| MYTHIC |

Some of the rarest weapons you will find are the **legendary golds** and **mythic yellows**. If you are fortunate enough to stumble across an RPG or SCAR assault rifle, do not pass it up, these are incredibly powerful weapons designed to wreak havoc.

TOP TIP

YOU CAN SEE HOW MUCH DAMAGE YOUR WEAPONS DO BY PRESSING 'UP' ON MOST CONTROLLERS TO ACCESS YOUR INVENTORY.

YOU'RE NOW ON YOUR WAY TO BECOMING A ONE-PLAYER ARMY.

SCAVENGER HUNT

START

STOPWATCHES AT THE READY!

THERE ARE TWO WAYS TO SOLVE THIS LABYRINTH. THE FIRST IS A SPEED RUN. HOW QUICKLY CAN YOU MAKE IT THROUGH?

THE SECOND HAS YOU STOPPING OFF AND COLLECTING ALL THE MATERIALS YOU CAN FIND. FIVE-SECOND PENALTY FOR EACH ITEM YOU MISS. ON YOUR MARKS, GO!

FINISH

23

Answers on page 75

SOLO, DUO AND SQUAD TACTICS

TOP TIPS TO HELP YOU WIN!

#1 **Find yourself a weapon.** Don't be picky. Without one you will be extremely vulnerable to any other player you come across.

#2 **Be quiet!** If your enemy detects you first, they have the advantage. Running is loud. Walk or crouch when you can.

#3 **Want to hear the enemy?** Headphones will give you the best chance, and help you know where the sound is coming from.

#4 **Stay inside the circle,** away from the storm. When the timer ticks down, being on the inside is key.

#5 **Drink shield potions** when you get them. You can get your shield to 100 by drinking two smalls and a regular, in that order.

#6 **Don't take on an enemy** unless you are sure you will win. Remember, the goal is to survive until the end.

#7 **When playing in duos or squads,** communication is key. Let your friends know what supplies you have and call for backup.

#8 **A team that lands together,** fights and survives together. Use landmarks to identify targets and all aim for the same spot.

#9 **Master building.** It is a key tactic used by the pros. In some cases, throwing up quick walls can act as infinite shields.

#10 **Don't loot victims straightaway.** Gunfights draw attention and everybody can see that attractive pile of fallen stash lying there.

FORTNITE WORDSEARCH

GREAT FORTNITE PLAYERS CAN SPOT THEIR ENEMIES A MILE OFF
AND KNOW WHERE TO LOOK IN ORDER TO DIG OUT THE BEST LOOT.
PUT YOUR SKILLS TO THE TEST WITH THIS WORDSEARCH.

```
R O Y A L E V A C H J G H L B
Q O V B M A T E R I A L S J A
E K C D C F C G L I D E R K T
T F W K R O B D C K K G B H T
G E D R E R U C H U G J U G L
D R I T A T V S C A V E N G E
S G O U T N L G V S I B N G B
P H F M I I O A K N T V T J U
I I O R V T O H U V H O R H S
O R C T E E T J H N G R R G H
B V N K G N B J G B C F A M G
C U I E A U G G Y F D H A F G
K Y T S J X N H T S D S E S H
O U E D H M E G S N I P E R K
B U I L D I N G I K L H G F C
```

FORTNITE   ROYALE   ROCKET LAUNCHER
SHOTGUN   BUILDING   BATTLE BUS
STORM   CREATIVE   SNIPER
SCAVENGE   GLIDER   PICKAXE
MATERIALS   CHUG JUG   LOOT

ANSWERS ON PAGE 76

THE NAME GAME

CREATE YOUR OWN UNIQUE FORTNITE CHARACTER NAME BY COMBINING THE WORD BESIDE THE FIRST LETTER OF YOUR FIRST NAME AND THE WORD BESIDE THE FIRST LETTER OF YOUR SURNAME.

FIND THE FIRST LETTER OF YOUR FIRST NAME:

A = GIANT	F = SNEAKY	K = FLOSSY	Q = HILARIOUS	V = ROYAL
B = SPIKEY	G = MYSTERIOUS	L = AWESOME	R = SUPER	W = LUCKY
C = CURIOUS	H = GIFTED	M = CLUMSY	S = POWERFUL	X = CLEVER
D = TINY	I = BRAVE	N = STINKY	T = COOL	Y = MEGA
E = AMAZING	J = RICH	O = ITCHY	U = UNRULY	Z = VICTORIOUS
		P = FURRY		

FIND THE FIRST LETTER OF YOUR SURNAME:

A = CAT	F = KNIGHT	K = PIZZA	Q = TREE	V = HERO
B = NERD	G = LLAMA	L = UNICORN	R = ARTIST	W = MUSHROOM
C = GNOME	H = VOYAGER	M = STAR	S = BEAR	X = BANANA
D = MOUSE	I = SHARK	N = TANK	T = DANCER	Y = JOKER
E = FIGHTER	J = BOULDER	O = EAGLE	U = WARRIOR	Z = BALLOON
		P = TURTLE		

MY FORTNITE CHARACTER NAME IS:

_____   _____

THE BATTLE PASS

WITH THE BATTLE PASS YOU CAN UNLOCK SPECIAL SEASON-RELATED SKINS AND WRAPS. EVEN BETTER, THE MORE YOU PLAY, THE GREATER THE REWARDS.

DESIGN YOUR OWN BATTLE PASS

Now you know how to unlock all that lovely loot, why not have a go at designing your very own Battle Pass, complete with the great skins, wraps and bonuses you'd love to see in Fortnite?

The best way to progress through the Battle Pass' 100 levels is to **gain XP**, and these tips will get you racing towards the max.

MAKE IT TO THE FIRST CIRCLE

If that means **avoiding busy crunch points** until you're a streaming pro, so be it.

PLAY WITH FRIENDS

Running with friends isn't just more fun, it gives you **extra XP**. The effect stacks, so a full squad grants a real boost. Even better, playing as a group helps your survival chances, giving you more XP at the end of each match.

COMPLETE CHALLENGES

Each season has about **70 daily challenges** to complete, that's **35,000 extra XP** just waiting for you.

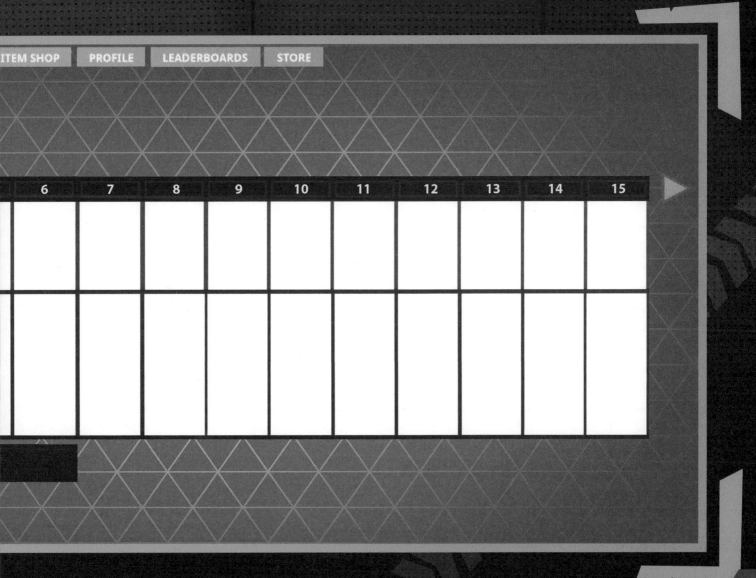

ITEM SHOP   PROFILE   LEADERBOARDS   STORE

6	7	8	9	10	11	12	13	14	15

BOUNTY HUNTER

ONE WAY TO BECOME A FORTNITE MASTER IS TO
HONE YOUR SKILLS WITH A SERIES OF TESTS.

Try each of the challenge cards and record how you have done to chart your progress. Some are as much about learning as they are about winning.

Get an adult to help you cut carefully around the dotted lines of the cards opposite and then shuffle the deck, before randomly selecting a different challenge to accept. **Ready up soldier!.**

	DIFFICULTY RATING	TIME TAKEN	ATTEMPTS MADE
1			
2			
3			
4			
5			
6			
7			
8			
9			

1
PEACE CORPS
SELF-DEFENCE ONLY
SHOOT WHEN SHOT AT

2
PISTOLS AT DAWN
YOU CAN ONLY PICK UP
AND USE PISTOLS

3
MATERIALISM
TRY TO PLAY
WITHOUT BUILDING
ANYTHING

4
ROWDY RACKET
NO CROUCHING
OR WALKING. RUN
EVERYWHERE

5
WHO NEEDS BUILDINGS?
YOU ARE NOT
ALLOWED INSIDE
ANY STRUCTURES

6
ILL COMMUNICATION
NO HEADSETS. YOU
CANNOT TALK WITH
ANY OTHER PLAYERS

7
LOOT IS FOR LOSERS
YOU CAN NOT PICK
UP ANY ITEMS SO
PICKAXES ONLY FOLKS

8
POTION MASTER
NO CHUG JUGS OR
ANY KIND OF MEDS

9
SPY MODE
SILENCED
WEAPONS ONLY

BOUNTY
HUNTER
PACK

BOUNTY
HUNTER
PACK

BOUNTY
HUNTER
PACK

BOUNTY
HUNTER
PACK

BOUNTY
HUNTER
PACK

BOUNTY
HUNTER
PACK

BOUNTY
HUNTER
PACK

BOUNTY
HUNTER
PACK

BOUNTY
HUNTER
PACK

FACT OR FICTION ?

PERFECT AIM AND BUILDING SKILLS ARE IMPRESSIVE ON THE BATTLEFIELDS OF FORTNITE BUT IN THE PLAYGROUND, KNOWLEDGE IS KING.

Test your understanding of the epic shooter with this fun true or false quiz. Once you've solved them yourself, why not try them on your friends?

#1 FORTNITE IS PLAYED BY 200,000,000 (TWO HUNDRED MILLION) PLAYERS AROUND THE WORLD.

#2 THE MORE MONEY YOU SPEND ON YOUR CHARACTER, THE BETTER THEY PERFORM IN THE GAME.

#3 BATTLE ROYALE WAS NOT SUPPOSED TO BE FORTNITE'S CALLING CARD.

#4 FORTNITE EARNED ABOUT £2 BILLION IN 2018.

#5 THE BEST WAY TO WIN AT FORTNITE IS TO CHEAT.

#6 FORTNITE WAS RUSHED OUT TO CASH IN ON THE GROWING POPULARITY OF ONLINE GAMING.

#7 YOU CAN PLAY FORTNITE WITH AND AGAINST YOUR FRIENDS NO MATTER WHAT SYSTEM THEY ARE PLAYING ON, EVEN IF IT'S DIFFERENT FROM YOURS.

#8 FORTNITE IS THE MOST STREAMED GAME ON TWITCH.

#9 THERE IS A FORTNITE WORLD CUP AND IT HAS A PRIZE POOL OF ABOUT £25 MILLION.

#10 THE RECON EXPERT SKIN IS FAMOUS BECAUSE IT IS SO RARE.

ANSWERS ON PAGE 76

TOP 10 SKINS
OF ALL TIME

★★★★★

DO YOU AGREE?

TOMATOHEAD

Classic fruit-on-head character. First released in Season 3 as part of the Pizza Pit Set.

P.A.N.D.A.

Legendary Outfit from Season 5. Keep an eye out for the limited edition Valentine Pink Bear.

FISHSTICK

A big hit since its Season 7 release. Fishstick even became the mascot of its own restaurant in the Craggy Hills.

GUFF

From the Chapter 2 Season 2 Mythical Might set, but your guess is as good as anybody else's as to what Guff is.

RAVEN

The mysterious Legendary skin from Season 3. Ravens are often associated with prophecies and insight.

PEELY

A reward for reaching Tier 47 of the Season 8 Battle Pass, Peely's popularity rivals that of Fishstick.

MIDAS

Those lucky enough to reach Level 100 in Chapter 2 were rewarded with this nifty villain.

RIPPLEY

Believe it or not this Slurp Squad hero is a friendly blob made of, you guessed it, slurp.

ASTRO JACK

Space-themed skin added in Chapter 2 Season 2. Pulses and glows when dancing.

BLAZE

Not to be confused with the Glider that shares its name. This came out in Chapter 2 Season 3 with the Lava Series.

KNOW YOUR WEAPONS

YOU'VE GOT YOUR FIRST WEAPON. THAT'S GREAT, DON'T STOP THERE.

Every weapon in Fortnite has its use, but if you are just beginning, look out for assault rifles and submachine guns. These are the most useful weapons, in most situations.

Snipers are for crack shots, shotguns rule at close quarters. Once you've got to grips with the basics, our weapons guide will have you firing on all cylinders.

SHOTGUNS

Keep a shotgun for close-up duels as few match their phenomenal stopping power. They often only need one shot to drop an opponent.

Shotguns typically come in heavy, pump or tactical forms, with other models making appearances depending on the season or game mode. Each has its own stats and feel but be careful as they have slow rates of fire, limited magazines, and long reload times.

Look out for the **ultra-rare Dragon's Breath** that fires every single shell at the same time and causes wooden buildings to catch fire. **OUCH!**

PISTOLS

Small, one-handed weapons that are often seen as a 'better than nothing' option.

They can be useful at medium range, away from the deadly blasts of shotguns, and can do considerable damage per second, but, and it is A BIG BUT, carry so few rounds you will be reloading in the middle of a lot of gunfights.

Some pistols are 'suppressed' - the technical term for silenced - useful for players who like to surprise their foes.

SNIPER RIFLES

The best way to stay alive in Fortnite is to steer clear of your enemies. The best way to knock them off at a distance, is with a sniper rifle.

Just make sure you have anything else to hand for when you get swarmed because snipers are next to useless up close.

Sniper rifles are powerful enough to bring enemies down in a single shot but have small magazines, slow rates of fire, and long reload times.

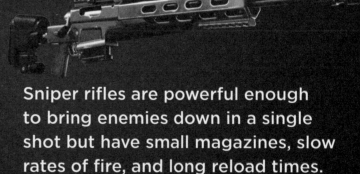

EXPLOSIVE WEAPONS

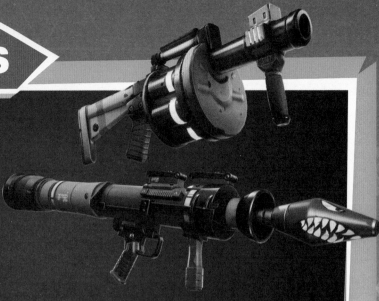

When the time comes to blow everything up, you will want to reach for a grenade or rocket launcher.

They are the perfect endgame weapons, especially when enemies are clustered together and the building bonanza has begun. These weapons can dish out devastating damage over a wide area.

The damage from the explosion is often enough to wipe out your opponents but don't waste your shots as ammo is in short supply and they are slow to reload.

TOP TIP

If you suspect a tower is packed with rival players, don't waste time trying to pick them off one by one. Use a grenade or rocket launcher to bring down the whole structure, taking everyone inside with it.

MELEE WEAPONS

If you've read this far you must really want to know everything there is about Fortnite's weapons and we salute you. However, Melee weapons should come with a health warning, yours! If you want something slow and weak you are in luck. They are called 'harvesting tools' for a reason. Best to find something, anything, quickly.

ASSAULT WEAPONS

This is more like it. Assault rifles are your workhorse medium-range machines that can still do a decent job close up or further away if you don't have anything better.

They can hold large magazines and fire very quickly, making them the perfect all-rounder, particularly if you are just starting out and haven't yet mastered all the weapons in Fortnite.

Assault weapons come in three main forms, standard, tactical, and heavy, each differing in damage and fire rates. In some game modes you can even add scopes to certain rifles and use them like snipers.

SUBMACHINE GUNS

Submachine guns (or SMGs to those in the know) are great rapid-fire weapons designed to hurl bullets across a wide area.

Think of them as insect swarms dealing out vast amounts of small damage that soon adds up. The tough part isn't hitting your opponent, because you certainly will, the skill is hitting them enough times to stop them in their tracks.

You can even find 'suppressed' SMGs to make a great pairing with any of your spy skins.

BONUS TIP

All weapons handle and fire differently. When starting out, use the ones you feel most comfortable with and practise with them. Learn their recoil patterns and how many shots they need to take out your enemies.

GET SET, SHOOT

A FORTNITE PRO ALWAYS CARRIES THE RIGHT TOOL FOR THE JOB.

By now you should be well on your way to learning about all the different weapons in Fortnite. So let's put that knowledge to the test.

Below are **three important missions** that call for a **special super soldier.** Are you ready for the challenge?

- ⊕ Follow your orders for each of the missions

- ⊕ All missions require you to start at the square marked X on the map

- ⊕ Whichever square your mission takes you to, is your firing position

- ⊕ Choose the right weapon depending on your distance from the mission target

- ⊕ Select either the close-up shotgun, a mid-range assault rifle, or the sniper rifle for long-distance shots

Target A :

Move five squares west, go eight squares south, sneak through two squares east, sprint four squares north, march one square east. You should be able to see the enemy. What weapon do you use?

Target B :

Move four squares south, go five squares west, run north for two squares to avoid enemy fire, swim for one square west. You can't get any closer, now's your chance, what weapon do you use?

Target C :

Sneak eight squares south fast. Then you will need to move quietly west for three squares. Now make your way north for one square and take out the enemy. What weapon do you think would be best?

FOLLOW THE INSTRUCTIONS ON PAGE 40, MARK WHERE YOU ARE SENT, AND THEN PICK YOUR WEAPON TO TAKE OUT YOUR TARGET.

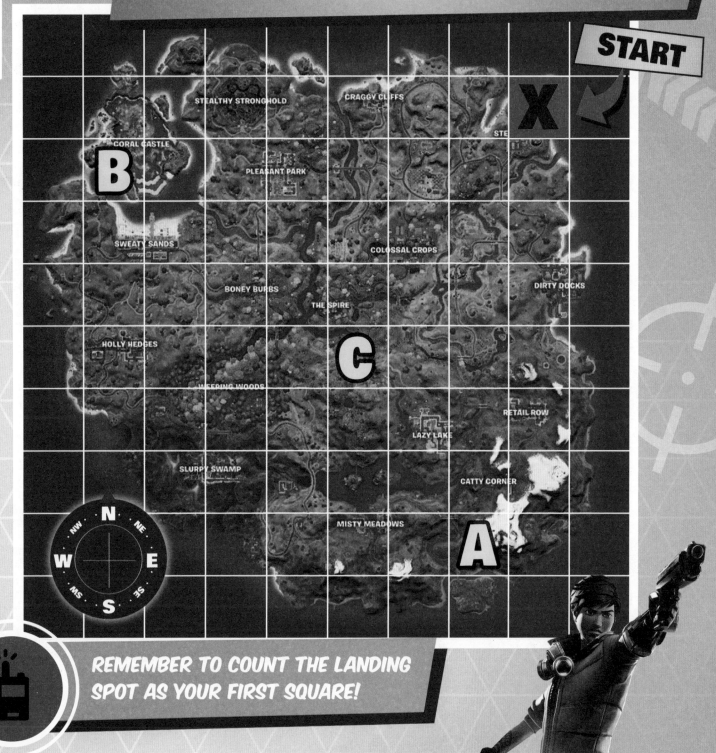

START

X

B

STEALTHY STRONGHOLD

CRAGGY CLIFFS

STE

CORAL CASTLE

PLEASANT PARK

SWEATY SANDS

COLOSSAL CROPS

BONEY BURBS

DIRTY DOCKS

THE SPIRE

HOLLY HEDGES

C

WEEPING WOODS

RETAIL ROW

LAZY LAKE

SLURPY SWAMP

CATTY CORNER

MISTY MEADOWS

A

N NE
NW
W   E
SW   SE
S

REMEMBER TO COUNT THE LANDING SPOT AS YOUR FIRST SQUARE!

SHOTGUN
SHORT RANGE: ONE SQUARE

★★★

ASSAULT RIFLE
MEDIUM RANGE: TWO SQUARES

★★★★

SNIPER RIFLE
LONG RANGE: THREE SQUARES

★★★★★

Answers on page 76

LEGENDARY, MYTHIC
AND JUST PLAIN GREAT WEAPONS

The SCAR

Ask a Fortnite veteran what's the best weapon and most will say the SCAR assault rifle. This ultra-dependable favourite deals out nearly 200 damage per shot. It's equally lethal over long distances as close up.

Jules' Drum Gun

The 40-round magazine means you can let the bullets fly freely. Eliminate Jules at The Authority and his gun is yours. Those extra shots make it ace at taking out towers.

Ocean's Burst Assault Rifle

What's better than hitting somebody with one shot. Two of course! The Ocean fires a two-burst pulse and its 222 damage per second puts this up there with some of the best in the game's history.

Bolt Action Sniper Rifle

Practice makes perfect but **OMG** is it worth it. Few weapons in Fortnite reward patience and effort as much as the bolt action sniper. Get your aim right and you're an unstoppable long-range player.

HINT: LEARN THE RECOIL PATTERNS OF YOUR RAPID-FIRE WEAPONS SO YOU KNOW WHERE TO AIM THAT FIRST SHOT

TOP TIP

Remember, over distances gravity has an effect on your shots. Aim just above where you want your shot to land.

Tactical Shotgun

As much a dream for you, as a nightmare for anybody foolish enough to stand in your way. A perfectly named weapon, if your tactics are to leap about, building and moving, while spamming the trigger.

Infinity Blade

Overpowered mythic melee weapon. Players would slash at their enemies, quickly cutting them down, and could destroy the environment in a single blow. Unsurprisingly, it was soon vaulted.

Rocket Launcher

Long-time players will remember rocket launchers with fondness for their tower-toppling prowess. These are fort-destroying machines that suit long-range battles, unless you're happy blowing yourself up too? Kaboom!

Minigun

If you want to use this master of disaster you'll need to hop over to Creative mode. But believe us, it's worth stepping away from Battle Royale for the opportunity to witness its devastating fire power.

Compact SMG

When you want to wipe out an entire room full of rivals, look no further. Use a compact SMG at close range and its spray-n-pray characteristics will spread panic wider than the bullets it spews.

Dragon's Breath Shotgun

This sinister serpent spits all four of its rounds at once, covering a vast area and causing massive damage. Want more? How about it also burns anything it hits so be careful it doesn't come back to bite you.

Last one standing. Jonesy is hiding and it is up to you to find him to claim top spot and a glorious Victory Royale. Using your sniper skills, can you scan this picture and locate the sneaky soldier's hiding spot?

Answer on page 76

WHICH WEAPON?

FORTNITE'S ISLAND IS A MASSIVE GALLERY OF GUNS AND GRENADES. UNDOUBTEDLY YOU WILL HAVE YOUR FAVOURITES AMONG THE PISTOLS, RIFLES AND ROCKET LAUNCHERS. WHILE THE THOUGHT OF PERMANENTLY VAULTING OTHERS MIGHT WELL FILL YOU WITH GLEE. HOWEVER, THERE IS A LOT MORE TO CONSIDER THAN JUST PERSONAL PREFERENCE WHEN CHOOSING A WEAPON.

EQUIPMENT

| 1 | 2 | 3 | 4 | 5 |

You only have room to carry up to **five** items at a time!

Inventory space is at a premium and will run out very quickly if you grab every gun going. You don't want to be defenceless in a survival game so after you have snagged a few weapons, you must be highly selective. The trick is to ensure you have the right balance to deal with any situation you might encounter.

Keep in mind that you also need to reserve slots for anything else you want to carry. **These include:**

HEALING KITS

SHIELD POTIONS

GREAT GRENADES

The Right Balance

To give yourself the greatest advantage and most balanced character you should carry three weapons MAX. This gives you options to cover most scenarios. A sniper rifle and a shotgun prepares you for both long- and close-range fights. Add an assault rifle, throw in a healing kit and a grenade, and there is really no stopping you.

THE GAME'S GREATEST WEAPONS ARE USUALLY BURIED DEEP WITHIN EACH MATCH AND OFTEN SUCCESS IS AS MUCH ABOUT YOUR LOADOUT AS THE HEAT YOU'RE PACKING.

That shiny pile of tempting weapons is certainly worth grabbing when you've first landed. Just as important though is knowing when to leave it. You can save yourself time and avoid needless risks if you run a balanced character. Let us explain. If you are already carrying a sniper rifle and see another one, is it worth taking enemy fire for a small upgrade? Probably not, but if it's a grenade launcher, that's a different story.

AMMO

 24  103  18  8  16

Good players track how many rounds they're carrying for each of their weapons. There are distinct ammo types in Fortnite and knowing how they pair with your arsenal is key. Light bullets are for pistols and SMGs, while shells only work in shotguns. Conserve ammo for your best weapons and whatever you do, don't waste precious rockets taking potshots at far off players. You can only carry a few at a time, so you don't waste them! Ammo is another good reason to carry different weapon types. If you're running low on your assault rifle, switch to a pistol and continue the fight.

DESIGN YOUR OWN WEAPON

WE THINK THE FORTNITE GAME DESIGNERS HAVE CREATED SOME PRETTY AWESOME WEAPONS IN THEIR TIME.

And... judging by the fact the game now has more than **350,000,000 players** worldwide, we're not the only ones! Do you think you have what it takes to create the next must-have Fortnite weapon?

Give it a go in the space below.

SHOTGUN

★★

Rarity:	DPS:
COMMON	63

Damage:	Fire Rate:
90	1.0

Magazine Size:	Reload Time:
7	4.8

THE SCAR

★★★★

Rarity:	DPS:
LEGENDARY	235.4

Damage:	Fire Rate:
36	5.5

Magazine Size:	Reload Time:
30	2.1

DPS: DAMAGE PER SHOT

☆☆☆☆☆

Rarity:	DPS:

Damage:	Fire Rate:

Magazine Size:	Reload Time:

AWESOME ARMOURY

TO BUILD YOUR ARSENAL OF WEAPONS, USE THE CLUES TO CORRECTLY FILL IN THE BOXES. CAN YOU WORK OUT THE KEY WORD?

#1 This small weapon is super-handy, because you only need one hand to hold it.

#2 With this weapon, hold down the button to send bullets flying in every direction.

#3 You can keep your distance and still make the shot with this long-range weapon.

#4 Pull the pin, then quickly take cover before this weapon goes BOOM!

#5 You don't need the best aim to make a big impact with this BIG weapon.

#6 Look down the barrel of this close-range weapon and into your enemy's eyes.

THE KEY WORD IS:

DO YOU KNOW YOUR WEAPONS?

You need to be fully equipped to take on all comers in Fortnite so let's make sure you know your pistols and rifles from your rockets.

ANSWER THESE SEVEN TOUGH PUZZLERS AND PROVE YOU'RE READY FOR THE BATTLE ROYALE!

#1 Name a small one-handed weapon that can get you out of a jam and can be good at helping you go undetected.

#2 Who needs to aim when you're carrying one of these heavy weapons? Just fire in the general direction and watch the fun.

#3 You can aim down the scope and pick off your enemies from across the map with this beauty.

#4 Running around with the trigger pulled, firing bullets in every direction is the way to go with this weapon.

#5 Not all weapons are guns, some have pins that you pull before being thrown.

#6 The ultimate short-range blaster that can take down your opponent in just one shot.

#7 Not only are these the best all-round weapon types, but some would argue the super-rare version is the best weapon in the game.

Answers on page 77

SCAVENGE AND BUILD PUZZLE

Next time a boring old grown up tries to tell you that Fortnite is not a good way to spend some family time, show them this. Get an adult to help cut around the edges of the lines to create your own epic jigsaw puzzle.

SCAVENGE AND BUILD PUZZLE

IMPORTANCE OF BUILDING

YOU THOUGHT FORTNITE WAS A SHOOTING GAME? THINK AGAIN. FORTNITE IS BUILDING FIRST, EVERYTHING ELSE IS SECOND.

WHAT SEPARATES THE BEST FROM THE REST ISN'T THEIR AIM, IT'S HOW QUICKLY AND EFFICIENTLY THEY BUILD. LUCKILY, THIS BOOK HAS YOU COVERED.

TOP TIP

Change your controller settings. Don't stick with the default layout. Switch to Builder Pro to give your construction skills an instant boost.

As the name suggests, Builder Pro will turn you into a building expert helping your speed and accuracy.

Activate Builder Pro by going to 'Settings' and selecting 'Builder Pro' under 'Configuration'.

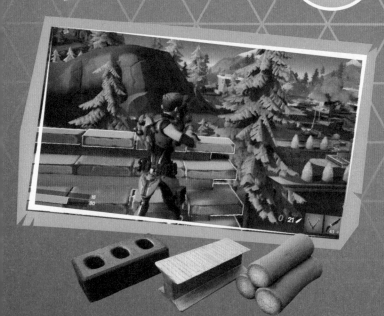

Learning to build helps you get to higher ground and those hard-to-reach places. This gives you a vital advantage. It lets you fire downwards on your enemies giving you a bigger target area, and that means **MORE DAMAGE.**

BAFFLING
BATTLE BUSES

CAN YOU SPOT THE TEN DIFFERENCES IN THESE TWO PICTURES?

SPOT THE DIFFERENCE

ANSWERS ON PAGE 77

DANCE OFF!

IT'S TIME TO SWITCH TO DANCE MODE AND SHOW OFF YOUR MOVES!

Throw the dice to select some emotes and then create your own Fortnite mid-battle routine.

HOW TO PLAY

1. Cast the dice 10 times and write down the numbers.
2. Every number on the dice matches an emote. Write down the 10 emotes you rolled.
3. Now put on your favourite song and do the moves!

YOU WILL NEED

ONE DICE

A DANCE PARTNER
(OPTIONAL)

1. FLOSS

2. CALL ME

3. DAB

4. CARTWHEELIN'

5. CRISS CROSS

6. BUCKETS

Need help with your flossing? Check out page 58

EPIC DANCE MOVES

#1 DEFAULT

If you've danced in Fortnite you know this dance, the aptly named default every player starts with. Overused? Maybe. A classic? 100%.

#2 TAKE THE L

Rub your opponents' demise in their defeated faces by pulling out a Take the Loss dance on top of their fallen avatar.

#3 THE WORM

Launching way back in Season 2, the Worm's mythic status has only grown with the passing of time. Those who got it, flaunt it.

#4 THE ROBOT

Old-school street dance got a new lease of life after being included in Fortnite. Sports stars have performed the dance celebrating goals.

#5 FRESH DANCE

Based on nerdy Carlton's hilarious moves on *The Fresh Prince of Bel-Air*. You actually need to be really talented to dance this badly.

#6 ORANGE JUSTICE

Internet campaign to get 'justice' for a kid in an orange t-shirt, who had lost a competition for his emote to be included in the game.

#7 ELECTRO SHUFFLE

One of the most popular emotes in Fortnite since its January 2018 release. The high-energy moves were inspired by a popular YouTuber.

#8 PHONE IT IN

Controversy followed the release of this emote after famous saxophonist Leo P said Fortnite's makers borrowed his moves.

#10 THE FLOSS

Performed around the world since its Season 2 launch, the Floss is no longer available. But don't worry you can still get flossing. Turn the page and we'll show you how to perform it!

#9 LLAMA BELL

If you want to play an instrument in Fortnite and annoy anybody within 10 feet of you, then the Llama Bell is the way to go.

HOW TO FLOSS

IF THERE IS ONE DANCE PEOPLE LINK WITH FORTNITE, IT'S THE FLOSS. THE CRAZY ARM-SWINGY DANCE HAS BEEN PERFORMED THE WORLD OVER BY COUNTLESS CELEBRITIES, SPORTS STARS, AND OF COURSE, SCHOOL KIDS.

Those new to flossing however, may wonder where or how to get in on the act; the dance is no longer available in Fortnite. If you were there, you were there.

Fear not, 100% Fortnite Unofficial guide has you covered. Just follow these easy steps and you'll be flossing the night away with the best of them.

#1

Stand with your feet shoulder-width apart. With your arms straight by your side, make fists with your hands like you're holding a rope, or dental floss, geddit?

#2

Keeping your arms straight, swing them both to your left. As you are doing this, push your hips to the right. If you can get both fists past your hips you're doing great!

#3

Swing your arms to the right and hips to the left but this time keep your left arm in front of your body, and right arm behind you. This is the 'behind' move.

#4

This next one shouldn't be that tricky. You just undo step 3 so that you are back to stage two! See how the arms are basically in the the same position as before.

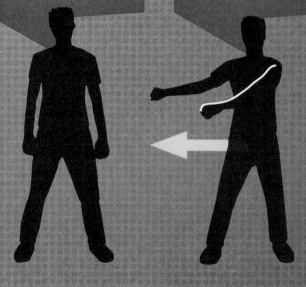

The tricky part is stitching it together. But if you can swing your arms one way and your hips the other, you'll get the hang of it in no time.

To help you visualise, think: 'Why is this dance called The Floss?'. You will get quicker with practice, and the faster you can do it, the cooler it looks.

THE KEY THINGS TO REMEMBER ARE:

Swing your hips side to side and 'back, forward, change' with your arms. Put them together and you've got the Floss.

TOP TIP

With practice you can start with your arms to the right to make your Floss even more impressive.

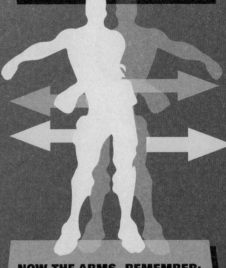

TO BEGIN, JUST MOVE YOUR HIPS FROM SIDE TO SIDE.

NOW THE ARMS. REMEMBER: BACK, FORWARD, CHANGE.

#5

Now it's time for the 'forward' stage. Simply swing your arms across the front of your body, with your hips going the other way. You need to floss both sides.

#6

Almost there! Time for another 'behind' but this time when you swing your arms to the left, keep your right arm in front of you and your left arm tucked behind.

#7

Last step, don't give up now! Swing your arms back to the right while pushing your hips to the left. Don't look now but **YOU'VE JUST DONE THE FLOSS!**

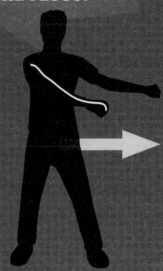

TOP TIP

Small hip movements make for faster flossing, but if you push them out further your dance will be more dramatic. Have a go at both and see what you like best, or try mixing and matching to make your own style.

FORTNITE FUN
10 EPIC JOKES

WHAT DO YOU CALL A DINOSAUR THAT PLAYS FORTNITE?

A FLOSSORAPTOR

WHAT DO YOU CALL 100 COWS PLAYING FORTNITE?

A CATTLE ROYALE

HOW DO YOU MAKE YOUR TV DANCE?

BY USING THE EMOTE CONTROL

HOW DO YOU PROVE YOU'VE SCORED A VICTORY ROYALE?

BY TAKING EPIC

HOW DID FORTNITE BECOME SO POPULAR?

BY TAKING THE WORLD BY STORM

WHY DO FORTNITE PLAYERS MAKE SUCH BAD TEACHERS?

THEY ALWAYS LET THE BATTLE PASS

WHY DOES KYLO REN ALWAYS PLAY DUOS?

BECAUSE HE DOESN'T LIKE SOLOS

HOW LONG DOES IT TAKE TO GET GOOD AT FORTNITE?

ABOUT TWO WEEKS

WHAT IS A DUCK'S MOTO IN FORTNITE?

BILLED BILLED BILLED

WHAT'S THE BEST PUDDING TO EAT FROM A DISTANCE?

SNIPER TRIFLE

BOOM!

BOOM!

OUTSIDE THE MAIN WEAPON CATEGORIES THERE ARE STILL PLENTY OF CLEVER AND INVENTIVE WAYS TO DEAL DAMAGE TO YOUR OPPONENTS.

One of the most common, and certainly more enjoyable, ways to make somebody 'go away' are grenades. Toss a handheld explosive at somebody and they will soon be your enemy, though they might not last too long. Stink bombs release clouds of damaging gas when they pop and you can also drop dynamite on the ground, which sets off when the timer ends.

Legendary | Ranged Weapon

GRENADE LAUNCHER

Ranged | Explosive Weapon

★★★★★

DPS 110.0	110.0
Damage	1.0
Fire Rate	6
Magazine Size	2.7
Reload Time	

Explosives are a great way to knock down enemy towers and structures. With aim and practice you'll be blowing up their lower levels in no time, causing the entire thing to topple. But wait, it gets even better. Not only have you just destroyed their battle fort, if it's high enough their subsequent tumble will cause a player fall damage. A drop of 23 metres or more is enough to wipe somebody out.

Not every weapon in Fortnite is portable. Very powerful mounted turrets can be attached to buildings and used to take out anyone stupid enough to storm your base. To take control of these brutal battlements just move them and press your 'use' button. Aim and fire as you would a standard weapon, and grin and smile knowing how much more damage you're capable of handing out. Just remember you can't move while firing so build some walls for protection.

Try playing with all the different weapon types in Fortnite to get a feel for them. You will naturally find you are better at using some than others but you might not find your favourites in a match so it's best giving them all a go. And, this being Fortnite, you can almost guarantee that just as you've got a handle on it all, the game's developers will add, tweak, nerf and vault the entire armoury.

BUILDING

BLOCKS

THE KEY MATERIALS OF FORTNITE

Knowing what material to use, whether that's wood, stone or metal, will give you an instant advantage over new players.

Walls, ramps, floors and roofs are all built the same way. The stronger the material, the longer it takes to build, and break.

TOP TIP

The best place to practise building is in Creative Mode, where you can let your imagination run wild without having to worry about being attacked.

"SETTINGS" ARE YOUR FRIENDS

Where possible, players should switch on Turbo Building and Automatic Material Swapping. Why? Turbo Building allows you to hold down the fire button to continuously build items quickly. Automatic Material Swapping will jump to the next available material if you run out of anything.

Wooden structures are quick to build, but also quick to be destroyed, so they are best used in emergencies rather than in the final circle.

Build powerful metal towers during the final circle when it's time to hunker down for the big showdown.

Use stone for when you want something more secure than wood but don't have the time, need, or materials for metal.

Keep your eyes peeled for traps that can be collected during matches for use on your opponents.

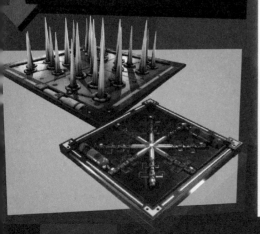

Each material has its own build time and health.

WOOD	STONE	METAL
		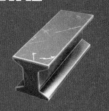
Wood panels take five seconds to build, with a starting health of 100 and a max health of 200.	Stone panels take 12 seconds to build, with a starting health of 90 and a max health of 300.	Metal panels take 20 seconds to build, with a starting health of 80 and a max health of 400.

BUILDER OF WORLDS

YOUR WORLD, YOUR RULES

Most players create small objects with the aim of making a quick barrier or escape route, but the tools in Fortnite allow for so much more. **Welcome to Fortnite's Creative mode.**

Here you will find all the tools needed to build your own universe and fill it with your favourite things. Creative even comes fully loaded with options not available in other game modes.

THE HUB

A circle of rocks, each with a rift. The first sends you to your own creation area, the others can take you to friends' zones or even featured locations which show off incredible new worlds.

ISLANDS

Players get four large open areas to build in. Inside these islands you can create anything you like, as long as it fits the set memory limit.

BUILD

In Creative, players are given a mobile phone that can copy, move or get rid of, well, anything. To begin, simply copya structure and place it anywhere you like. When you want to use something different, just pick a new one and repeat the process.

PREFABS

Wait? Copy structures? Yes. This is where Creative is different. There is an enormous menu of previously made items that players will recognise from the main game. These can be copied or tweaked. We're not just talking buildings either. Everything from shelves to kitchen sinks are included for you to do with as you please.

GAME MODES

If building your worlds is great, then adding your own game modes to them is the next level. Anything goes, whether that is free-for-all rumbles, timed races or tricky puzzlers. Creative mode turns Fortnite upside down and takes it to wherever your imagination leads. You can even join forces with your friends and work together!

FLY MODE

Unlike the traditional game modes, in Creative you can quickly zoom across your island or even create on the fly.

BUILD FOR VICTORY

PANIC WALL

Great for grabbing those crucial added seconds to duck behind while you reload, heal, or just straight up flee.

PANIC RAMP

A quickly built ramp during close combat will get you above your opponent or help you duck out of sight for even more protection.

V-SHAPED RAMP

Panic ramps with two sets of stairs opposite each other to form a 'V'. At the top of towers they create perfect vantage points.

SNIPER TOWER

Box yourself in with walls then add a ramp to move higher up. Repeat to build a skyscraper, now add a V-shaped ramp.

TOP TIP

The stronger the building material in your base, the harder it is to shoot it down - and send you tumbling to your doom.

HEALING ROOM

A place to hide and heal. Surround yourself with four walls and a roof for those precious extra seconds to med up.

WARNING:

Launch pads must be placed on a floor tile and for goodness sake build them away from trees or buildings.

WARNING:

Healing Rooms stand out and attract attention so don't linger too long otherwise they will quickly turn into hurt lockers.

LAUNCH PAD

Epic rare item that hurls you into the air so you can use your glider to quickly escape enemy attacks or the oncoming storm.

BOUNCER TRAP

Used to launch players off high places such as mountains or sniper towers while avoiding fall damage.

DAMAGE TRAP

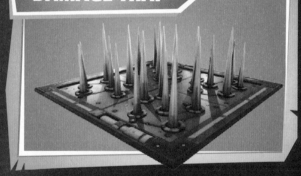

Best placed inside a house or fort for unsuspecting players to stumble across, or dropped on your rivals.

COZY CAMPFIRE

Healed two hit points per second for 25 seconds. Sharing these was a surefire way to become popular.

TOP TIP

Build a door at the bottom of your tower with a trap inside it and revel in your victim's downfall as they try to sneak after you.

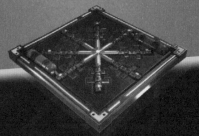

SCAVENGER SCRAMBLE

LOOK AT THE CLUES BELOW AND UNSCRAMBLE THE WORDS TO FORM KEY FORTNITE BUILDS.

1. CANAL WIPL

CLUE: Throw this up in a hurry for a quick shield

2. RAMPAGED TA

CLUE: Put this inside a house and laugh as your foes stumble across it

3. RIPENS WROTE

CLUE: Take out your enemies from this tall structure

4. SHAPED VRAMP

CLUE: Bird's nest on top of a tower

5. HALE MOORING

CLUE: Perfect for a spot of rest and relaxation

6. LUNCH DAAP

CLUE: For when you need to make a very quick getaway

7. NAPI CRAMP

CLUE: Run up and down this for quick and easy cover

8. TURBOCAR PEN

CLUE: Fling yourself off high places

9. EPIC MAZY FORC

CLUE: Turn to this when you need to rest up

Answers on page 77

MAZE RUNNERS

WHICH OF OUR HEROES AVOIDS THE TRAPS AND MAKES IT ALL THE WAY TO THE LOOT? ONLY ONE FORTNITE FIGHTER HAS WHAT IT TAKES TO MAKE IT.

Follow the lines and avoid any nasty surprises but who makes it all the way? Who gets the V-bucks?

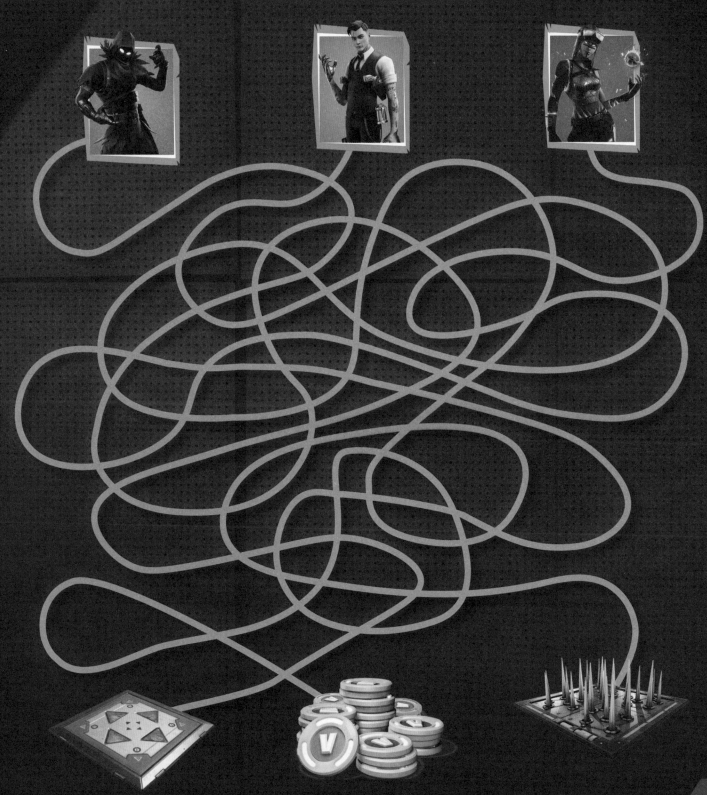

Answers on page 77

SHARP SHOOTER

CAN YOU SPOT THE TEN DIFFERENCES BETWEEN THESE TWO PICTURES?

TEST YOUR NO-SCOPE SKILLS

71

DREAM LOOT

FORTNITE'S THREE BUILDING MATERIALS OPEN UP A WORLD OF IMAGINATION.

If you were in charge, what you would add to the game?
Now draw your new building to show it off to your friends.

FORTNITE YOUR WAY

READY TO RUMBLE

KEEP OUT!

NON-GAMERS BEWARE!

ANSWERS

Page 16 **STAY INSIDE THE STORM**

Page 15 **HUNT FOR GEAR**

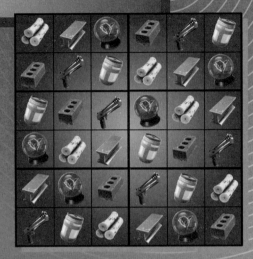

Page 18 **ODD ONE OUT**

1

3

2

4

Page 22
**SCAVENGER
HUNT**

START

FINISH

ANSWERS

Page 26
FORTNITE WORDSEARCH

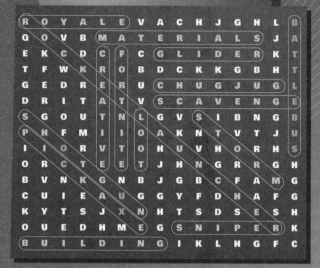

Page 44 WHERE'S JONESY?

Page 33 FACT OR FICTION?

#1 FICTION
FORTNITE IS PLAYED BY MORE THAN 350,000,000 PEOPLE. THAT MAKES IT BIGGER THAN NETFLIX.

#2 FICTION
SKINS AND WRAPS EXIST TO LET YOU MAKE YOUR AVATAR REFLECT YOUR OWN MOOD OR PERSONALITY THEY DON'T MEAN YOU WILL BE A BETTER PLAYER.

#3 FACT
FORTNITE WAS DESIGNED TO BE A BUILDING GAME WITH A HORDE MODE. THE BATTLE ROYALE EXPLOSION CAUGHT THE WORLD BY SURPRISE.

#4 FACT
JUST SHOWS THE AMAZING DRAWING POWER OF A FUN GAME THAT LETS YOUR IMAGINATION RUN WILD AND PROVIDES HAIR-TRIGGER THRILLS.

#5 FICTION
CHEATERS GET BANNED. THE GAME'S CREATOR HAS EVEN BEEN KNOWN TO TAKE LEGAL ACTION AGAINST PLAYERS SUSPECTED OF CHEATING.

#6 FICTION
DEVELOPERS EPIC GAMES BEGAN WORKING ON FORTNITE IN 2011, IT DIDN'T GET LAUNCHED UNTIL 2017. NOW, THAT'S DEDICATION!

#7 FACT
YOU CAN FORM YOUR OWN SUPER SQUADS NO MATTER WHAT PLATFORM YOUR BUDDIES ARE PLAYING ON. HOW COOL IS THAT?!

#8 FACT
AT PEAK TIMES MORE THAN 650,000 AVID FANS TUNE IN TO WATCH FORTNITE STREAMS, MAKING IT MORE POPULAR THAN SOME TV SHOWS.

#9 DOUBLE FACT
THAT'S RIGHT. PLAYERS FIGHT OVER A WHOPPING ₤25 MILLION PRIZE POOL, WITH A TOP PRIZE OF ₤2.5M FOR THE BEST SOLO PLAYER.

#10 FACT
IT WAS RELEASED IN OCTOBER 2017 WHEN FEW PEOPLE PAID FOR SKINS. DESPITE ITS SIMPLE LOOK, IF YOU HAVE IT, YOU STAND OUT.

Page 40
GET SET, SHOOT

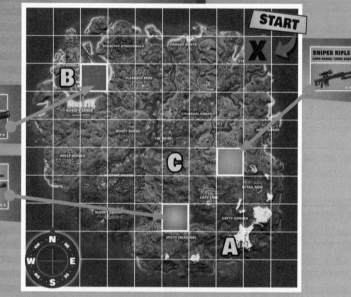

Page 49
AN AWESOME ARMOURY

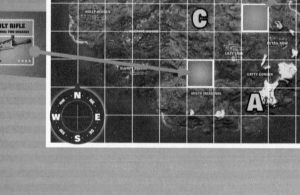

#1 PISTOL
#2 MACHINEGUN
#3 SNIPERRIFLE
#4 GRENADE
#5 ROCKETLAUNCHER
#6 SHOTGUN

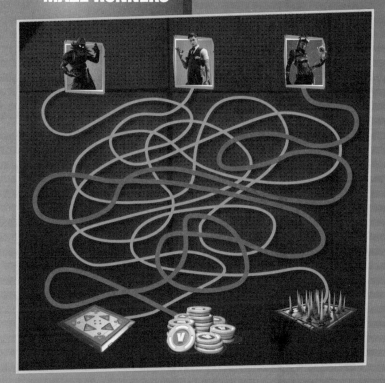

HOW DID YOU DO?!

Top Ten Tips for Keeping it Safe and Keeping it Fun!

#1 Never, ever, ever tell anyone your real name – don't use it as your username either!

#2 Don't tell anyone your age, school or address

#3 Don't give out any other personal info – about you, your friends or your family

#4 Your passwords are there to keep you safe – don't share them with anyone (except your parents or carers)

#5 There are lots of websites where you need to be over 13 to create an account. ALWAYS ask your parents or carers for permission before registering for websites

#6 If something doesn't feel right, it probably isn't right. Always share worries with your parents or carers

#7 Always be kind online. If someone is mean to you, tell your parents or carers straightaway. Remember it's always supposed to be fun!

#8 Take lots of breaks from gaming and the screen, the best players know that rests and real-life skills make them better gamers!

#9 It is better to play in shared spaces or close to your parents or carers

#10 Remember you don't need to spend money to have fun online

Note *FORTNITE: BATTLE ROYALE* is rated PEGI 12